The Plague
and
Doctor Caim

The Plague
and
Doctor Caim

Written & Illustrated by
G. E. Gallas

CAST
IRON
BOOKS

This edition first published in 2021

Cast Iron Books, 17 Clarence Street, Ulverston, Cumbria, LA12 7JJ

www.castironbooks.com

© G.E. Gallas

Written and Illustrated by: G.E. Gallas

A CIP record for this book is available from the British Library

ISBN: 978-1-8382241-2-7 (hardback)
ISBN: 978-1-8382241-3-4 (ebook)

1 2 3 4 5 6 7 8 9

W hen I began writing *The Plague and Doctor Caim* in 2016, I never imaged I would finish drawing it during a global pandemic.

I never imagined I would read about experimental treatment after treatment, much in the same vein as the trial and error practiced by the plague doctors of old.

I never imagined masks would become part of our daily lives. And I couldn't help but muse how the beak mask was no doubt a precursor to our antiviral ones.

I never imagined how the plague doctor costume would return as a symbol of our current predicament, cosplayers and even Halloweeners flooding our social media feeds – one teenage "plague doctor" went as far as to frequent a sleepy U.K. village, frightening the locals enough to earn a talking to from the police.

Coronavirus has been frustrating, devastating, and heart-rending on a scale the entire world could have never imagined before.

The vast majority of us are in mourning for lost loved ones, or loved ones of loved ones. Or, at the very least, we are in mourning for the hundreds of thousands who have lost their lives.

But, perhaps in a few centuries, we'll be able to find a pinch of humor in all this sorrow. Just in the same way I have found humor in the Bubonic plague and Doctor Caim.

– G.E. Gallas, 2021

Dear Dr. Caim:
Our town needs you.

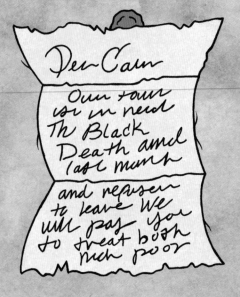

The Black Death arrived last month and refuses to leave.

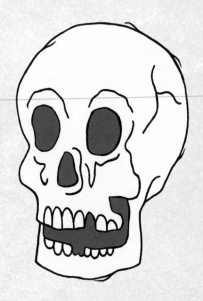

We will pay you to treat both the rich and the poor.

I would do so anyway.

2

I am ready, I think.

That is indeed
The Black Death.

11

18

21

24

32

33

41

43

45

56

58

64

Cherries!?

No beer, no mutton loin,
no cucumbers, no eels...

And, above all,
no cherries!!

67

73

83

The **Craft of Dying**

The Devil is busy to avert man from faith at his end.

Whoso taketh sickness or death with sorrow, it is a sign he loveth not God sufficiently.

It is not sorrow I have... I have no word sufficient for it.

Our heartfelt thanks to the Unbound backers listed below,
who have been with this book since the very beginning.

Thank you for your patience.

Buket Akgün

Saqr Al Qassimi

Elijah Aldana

Anya Alford

Mohammad AlHuraiz

Ahlyah Ali

Eli Allison

Charlotte Altass

Amy Andujar

Caren Ann Appel

Milo Applejohn

Sunny Asaf

Tony B.

Sierra Barnes

Rebecca Barr

Zena Barrie

Karen 'Kit' Baston

George Bastow

Jim & Samantha Bean 覆面豆

Nicholas Beckett

Angel Beckett

Kevin Berland

Izzy Berlin

Stacey Bethell

Ian Bird

Katharine Bittner

Dawn Bond

Becca Bradford

Nicholas Branch

Alice Broadribb

Scott Broom

Donna Brown

Emma Bull

Jane Burns

Colin Caccamise

Ashley Callahan

Cindi Camarillo

Brandon Carbaugh

Crimson Carousel

Jacqui Castle

Ioana Cerasella Chis

Dr. Cevraxion

Becky Chantry

Stefano Checchia

Mark Ciccone

Sue Clark

Sean Cleary

Jason Cobley

Jordan Collver

RYC Comics

Kelly Connolly

Jude Cook

Anthony Cooke

Samuel Craig

Mason Dante Stensrud

Paul Davies

Christian De Matteo

Rachel Dentinger

Katherine Dickerson

Nina Diener

Paul Dobbins

Samuel Dodson

Izzi Doherty

Jessica Duchen

Andrea Dworkowski

Tracy Edmunds

Felix Egadrik

Shah Emami

Katherine Emmel

John Emslie

Jonathan Evans

M.J. Fahy

Veinity Fair

Thomas Fitch

Kyle Forrest

Carrie Fox

Billi French

Richard Furniss

Leonardo Gada

Irene Gallas

Philip Gallas

Sydney Gallas

Shaun Gardiner

Jared Gardner

Angelo Garizzone

Gwenn Garland

Elizabeth Geelan

Emma Grae

Karen Green

Delaine Green

Josephine Greenland

Geoffrey Gudgion

Bethany Hall

Owen Hammer

Vincent Harris

Maximilian Hawker

Heavenir

Untitled Hero

Sarah Hiltner

Heather Hobart

Tina Hoggatt

Robin Hummel-Fuller

Craig Hurd-McKenney

Noah Infusino

Alice Jaggers

Eunsoo Jeong

Reay Jespersen

Roland Johnson

Martin Johnston

Owen Kahn

Suzanne Karr Schmidt

Richard Kemp
Marc Kevin Hall
Ania Kierczynska
Norman Konyu
Ralph Lachmann
Ben Lacy
Stephen J. Lazotte
Anna Le
Shelby Liddicoet
Wayne Livingston
Elena Lopez
Julia Lundman
Edmund Lyon
Rob MacAndrew
Iffy Maduka
Jonah Malamud
Kristen Malick-Hatta
Annika Mann
GMarkC
Goblin Marketer
Andrew Marsh
Bethany Martin
Daniel Mawhinney
Lucy McCahon
Fiona McGavin
Hannah Meiklejohn
Michael Michael Thomas Lucio
Kyo Moller
Nadia Lee Monaghan
Kevin Moore
Melanie Moss
Eleni Nasiotis
Elizabeth Nelson
Ian Newman
Anh "Kai" Nguyen
Don Nguyen
Tommy Noodle
Ben North
Paul Noth
Gramps Oldman
Travis Ord

Joel Orff
Kate Orson
Francis Osis
Gary Ostroff
R P
Victoria Pearson
Kevin Petker
Craig Phillips
Allison Piazza
Cheryl Picard
Amanda Piercey
Rose Pleuler
Evan Pokroy
Avery Polinori
Kat Pope
Alice Pow
Heather Prescott
Nathan Pride
Shadowmark Productions
Caroline Pulver
Michael D. Purzycki
Kimberly R.
Kinley Raftery
Gabi Ramsey
Joad Raymond
Will Reno
Michael Rhode
James Rider
Nicola Rimmer
Mike & Parker Rizzo
Jill Robin Anderson
Aaron Sammut
Victoria Santamorena
Tom Scallon
Ericka Schenck
Jeremiah Schiek
Louise Schoenhult
Carl Sciacchitano
Addison Scott
Ste Sharp
Michael Sharp

Mickey Sheridan
Abigail Siegel
Stella Sigal
Dan Smith
Jamie Smythe
Spencer Soares
Jennifer Spirko
Angie Steiner
Erica Stensrud
Sarah Stevenson
David Stewart
Stephen Stratton
Cayley Sublette
Ben Taylor
Steve Thompson
Robert Tienken
Hildegunn Traa
Vincent Treptow
Emily Turner
Luna Valuna
Steve Venright
Alysia Viscanti
Mary Wagner
Eleanor Walsh
Tom Ward
Julia Webb-Harvey
Jason Whittaker
Lisa Whittingham
Laura Williams
Arnold Williams
Tricia Wirtanen Miller
Laura Wood
Deborah Wood
Tom Woodman
Dan Brotzel, Martin Jenkins &
   Alex Woolf
Natalie Wright
Aila Yeatts
Kim Zimmer
Mimi Zweig